Be UNAPOLOGETICALLY Who You Are

A Journal from

Jessica Butts

ISBN: 978-0-9992884-9-8

Design by Milena Hrebacka
NewBreed.Design

Printed by Gorham Printing in the United States of America

Legacy **ONE** AUTHORS

Kirkland, WA
www.legacyoneauthors.com

Welcome to the
Be UNAPOLOGETICALLY Who You Are
Journal

This journal was created to help you keep all your important Front Seat Life™ tools in the same place you keep your beautiful thoughts and feelings!

I speak to my clients all over the world about three main things when designing a life that works.

Who are you?
- Your innate personality Type

Where are you going?
- Uplevling your Mindset and getting clear on your ideal life

How are you going to get there?
- Taking Action with my Three S Method™: Structure, Systems and Singular Focus

One of the main areas I focus on is a morning practice which includes daily journaling. My clients finally nudged me to create a journal to keep all these things in one place. This journal is the result of that nudge, I hope you love it.

This journal is for those who want to live outside the confines of what society tells you to be doing with your life! I hope that this journal will help you become more of YOU! One of the best ways to start doing that is to keep a record of how you feel and what you think.

There are three main benefits of journaling:

1. Externalize the crazy (don't be offended, we all have it)
2. Ground yourself
3. See patterns in your life by rereading once or twice a year

There are LOTS of videos on my website about journaling and the rest of my morning practice at: **www.jessicabutts.com**

This journal is for the beginner as well as the A+ journaler and it is designed for those who want to *thrive*, not simply survive this life.

My hope is that this journal finally gives you permission to do whatever you want to do with your life because guess what? It is YOUR life! I don't know about you, but I want to use my time on this earth to do the absolute most I can with it. Do you long to have more fun, be creative, wake up early because you can't wait to tackle the day, travel, help people, be powerful, laugh more, change lives, connect, speak your truth, do the work you are meant to do, and leave a legacy for your family? You must start by journaling!

In order to get clear about your life, love and business, you MUST get to know yourself first! You need to design your life, not let life design it for you.

My **BHAG (Big Hairy Audacious Goal)** is to get everyone to start living according to **who you are**, not who other people want you to be. This alone will change your life. So, are you ready to get started on discovering YOU and Being Unapologetically Who You Are? Awesome! Enjoy your beautiful journal!

~ Jessica Butts

Section 1:
Who Are You?

Core Values

Theme Words

Front Seat & Back Seat

Personality Type

Love Languages

Gratitudes

Section 1: Who Are You?
DIRECTIONS:

Core Values:

Please visit JessicaButts.com Resources page to find the directions and printable core values exercise. Once you have your 3-7 core values, list them here and bounce every decision off of these before you say yes or no.

Theme Words:

What is your theme word or words for this year or this quarter? I usually have three but you may only need one. **LIVE BY THEM!**

Front Seat and Back Seat and Personality Type:

Use the diagram on page 8 as a reminder of all your amazing, innate, front seat activities and things you ROCK at, as well as what to avoid! It is placed here in your journal to remind you daily to "Be Unapologettically who you are" and "Don't do Stuff You Suck at"! If you don't know what this is yet, take the free assessment on my website and you might want to also pick up my books at **www.jessicabutts.com**

Love Languages:

Gary Chapman's book, *The 5 Love Languages* is a MUST! Remind yourself daily what YOUR love languages are and use the extra pages to write down your loved ones Love Languages as well. This tool can make a **HUGE** difference in the satisfaction of your relationships, which is all part of being unapologetically who you are!

Gratitudes:

Starting your day on the right note and being thankful for what you have sets the stage for your ENTIRE day. So, take a few moments each day to reflect on the things you are most grateful for because what you focus on GROWS!

Notes:

Your Core Values

_____
_____
_____
_____
_____
_____
_____
_____

Theme Words

_____
_____
_____
_____
_____
_____
_____
_____
_____
_____

Front Seat & Back Seat

Driver

Co-Pilot

Drunk Uncle
in the backseat

Baby in the
backseat

Your Personality Type

Notes:

Your Love Languages

Gratitudes

Section 2:
Where Are You Going?

Goal Cards

Mind Mapping

Section 2: Where Are You Going?
DIRECTIONS:

Goal Cards:

Goal cards changed my life and I know they can for you, too!

Goal Cards are a written version of your vision board so DREAM BIG! Goal cards are meant to be written as if:

- You already have "it"
- Or you attain it "easily and effortlessly"

You should always write your goals with positive language, and then read them aloud each day. If you want an actual set of goal cards they can be found on my website under the Shop tab. There are also some examples of my personal goal cards on my website and in my books.

Mind Mapping:

Mind Mapping is an excellent way for Intuitive (N) Types to get organized with their plans for the future. We are big picture, visual people and therefore getting our ideas out on a mind map is excellent for organization and planning. I have provided an outline here as well as extra pages for you to make your own. You can see examples of mind mapping on my website or simply Google it.

Notes:

Goal Cards

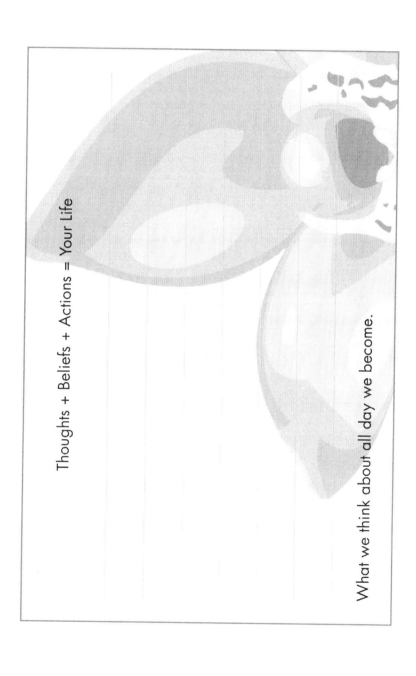

Thoughts + Beliefs + Actions = Your Life

What we think about all day we become.

Goal Cards

Thoughts + Beliefs + Actions = Your Life

What we think about all day we become.

Notes:

Goal Cards

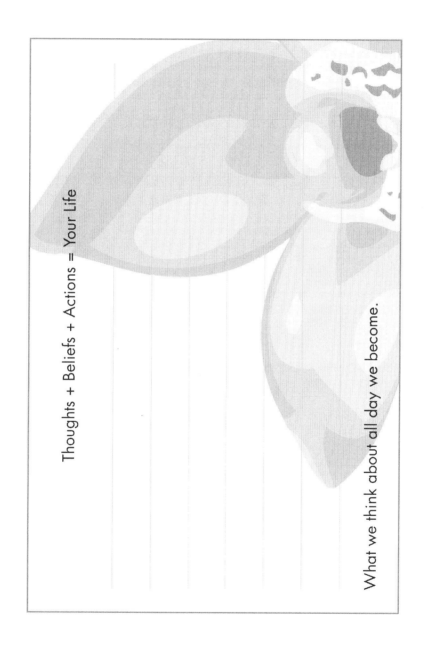

Thoughts + Beliefs + Actions = Your Life

What we think about all day we become.

Mind Mapping

YOUR **BIG** IDEA

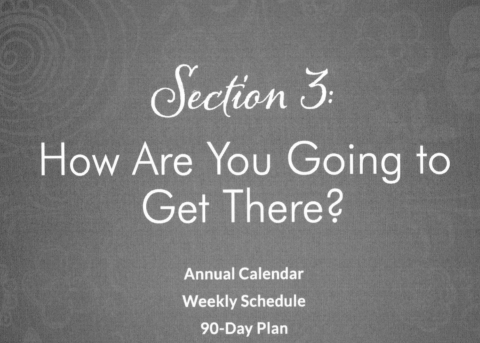

Section 3:

How Are You Going to Get There?

Annual Calendar

Weekly Schedule

90-Day Plan

Section 3: How Are You Going to Get There?

DIRECTIONS:

This section is all about not living 5 minutes in front of your face but really making a **PLAN** and taking **ACTION!** You can do this! It will change your life and business.

Annual Calendar:

One of the first steps to a successful life and business is to plan big events way in advance and work around those. Please use this calendar to list holidays, birthday's, trips, etc. For those of you who own your own business and are part of my Front Seat Life Business coaching program, this is where you schedule your large events and launches. We MUST be strategic and thoughtful in our launches.

Weekly Schedule:

This is an eye opening experience for most of my clients. They let their schedule dictate their life, not the other way around. We MUST be in control of our own schedule and prioritize our time around our "rocks" (theory first brought to us by the Stephen Covey) which are the most important things in our lives: ourselves, our partners, kids, downtime, work time, CEO meetings, best friends, front seat activities and things that bring us joy!

90-Day Focus:

One of my favorite tools of all time to stay on task! We are all inundated by TONS of opportunities, people, bright/shiny objects, and we may want to jump from one thing to the next without finishing our tasks at hand because it isn't as much fun but... **WE MUST!** In order to be a long term success in life or business we must give three things a quarter our full attention before we move on to the next. It is like building a house; we need to make sure we have a solid foundation before we decorate the rooms. **DO THIS. It will change your life!.**

Major Events

JANUARY	FEBRUARY
MARCH	APRIL
MAY	JUNE

Major Events

JULY	AUGUST

SEPTEMBER	OCTOBER

NOVEMBER	DECEMBER

Weekly Schedule

TIME BLOCKING RULES:

☐ Business
☐ Downtime
☐ Morning Practice

☐ Start with your Rocks
☐ A-List
☐ Family
☐ You

	MONDAY	TUESDAY	WEDNESDAY
5:00 am			
5:30 am			
6:00 am			
6:30 am			
7:00 am			
7:30 am			
8:00 am			
8:30 am			
9:00 am			
9:30 am			
10:00 am			
10:30 am			
10:30 am			
11:00 am			
11:30 am			
12:00 pm			
12:30 pm			
1:00 pm			
1:30 pm			
2:00 pm			
2:30 pm			
3:00 pm			
3:30 pm			
4:00 pm			
4:30 pm			
5:00 pm			
5:30 pm			
6:00 pm			
6:30 pm			
7:00 pm			

THURSDAY	FRIDAY	SATURDAY	SUNDAY

"I stopped waiting for the light at the end of the tunnel
...and lit that bitch up myself."

90-Day Plan

SPECIFIC GOAL	MOST IDEAL OUTCOME	KEY QUESTIONS/OBSTACLES	FIRST ACTION STEP
1.			
TARGET DATE:			
2.			
TARGET DATE:			
3.			
TARGET DATE:			

27

"Her intuition was her favorite superpower."

"Be fierce."

"Get at it, girl!"

"Life is tricky, baby; stay in your magic."

"Not everyone is going to like you – get over it."

"Eat like you love yourself."

"Decide what you want. Make a fucking plan, and work on that shit. Every. Single. Day."

"Once upon a time, you were a little girl with big dreams that you promised you'd make real one day. Don't disappoint yourself."

"It's difficult to follow your dream It's a tragedy not to."

"Be fearless in the pursuit of what sets your soul on fire."

"As soon as you begin to pursue a dream, your life wakes up and everything has meaning." ~ BARBARA SHER

"Stop being afraid of what could go wrong and think of what could go right."

"Don't chase people — attract them!"

"Be different, Babe."

"Be fearlessly authentic."

"You will never influence the world by being just like it."

"I would rather die of passion than boredom" ~ VAN GOGH

"Prove them wrong"

"The ones that are crazy enough to think they can change the world are the ones that do."

"Wherever you are, be all there."

"Be you. The world will adjust."

"Trust your gut."

"Surround yourself with people who get you."

"Dream Believe. Achieve."

"You're not tired You're uninspired."

"You won't succeed unless you try."

"Make yourself a priority."

"Actually, I can."

"It won't be easy, but it'll be worth it."

"Raise your standards and the universe will meet you there."

"Just a girl who decided to go for it."

"Success is a decision."

"Surround yourself with inspiring beings."

"A strong woman looks a challenge in the eye, and gives it a wink" — GINA CAREY

"I want to make myself proud."

"There is no force more powerful than a woman determined to rise."

"Be you. Do you. For you."

"I love the person I've become because I fought to become her"

"Find yourself and be that."

"Be yourself. People don't have to like you, and you don't have to care."

"Don't stop until you're proud."

"It's not your job to like me, it's mine." ~ BYRON KATIE

"Work like a boss."

"This is the part where you find out who you are."

"Once upon a time, you were a little girl with big dreams that you promised you'd make real one day. Don't disappoint yourself."

"Even if you don't feel like doing it, get that shit done."

"Be fearless in the pursuit of what sets your soul on fire."

"Great things never came from comfort zones."

"Love the shit out of yourself."

"She believed she could, so she did"

"You attract what you believe you deserve."

"You can't have a million dollar dream with a minimum wage work ethic."

"Underestimate me. That'll be fun."

"Positive Thinking = Positive Outcome."

"There's no way I was born to just pay bills and die."

"You're always one decision away from a totally different life."

"Let go. Be guided. Expect miracles."

"Let your past make you better, not bitter"

"Know thyself."

"Just breathe."

"You will never go broke from investing in yourself."

"I give myself permission to be powerful."

"Chill, homie. You need to let that shit go."

"Freedom is being You without anyone's permission."

"Stop holding yourself back. If you're not happy, make a change."

"You owe yourself the love that you so freely give to other people."

"She needed a hero, so that's what she became."

"Little girls with dreams become women with vision."

"The secret to your future is written in your daily routine."

"Once in a while, blow your own damn mind."

"She was unstoppable. Not because she didn't have her own failures or doubts but because she continued on despite them."

"Be you. The world will adjust."

"Don't do stuff you suck at!"

"I'm an odd combination of 'really sweet' and 'don't mess with me.'"

"Be addicted to the feeling of having your shit together."

"Embrace your weird."

"You know all those things you've always wanted to do?
You should go do them."

"You have to be odd to be number 1." ~ DR. SEUSS

"*Above all, be the heroine of your life, not the victim.*" ~ NORA EPHRON

"Seek respect, not attention It lasts longer."

"You did not wake up today to be mediocre."

"If there's one thing I'm willing to bet on, it's myself." ~ BEYONCÉ

"It's about the journey, not the destination."

"Begin again."

About the Author

Jessica is a retired psychotherapist turned life and business coach, author, speaker, and trainer. She is on a global mission to help people start living according to their personality type, be unapologetically who they are, and live happier, more authentic and richer lives. In her business coaching, keynotes and corporate trainings she teaches audiences three steps: (1) understand and embrace their innateness using the Myers-Briggs Type Indicator® and the Front Seat Life system, (2) up-level their mindset, and (3) take action using the Three S Method. Jessica is an ENFJ and passionate about many things in her life including deep connections with friends and family, Hawaii, sunsets, travel, and inspiring others to Live their Lives from the Front Seat.